Dear Reader,

My name is Frances Seaton. I am in the 8th grade at Owensboro Middle School. I take part in many extracurricular activities including KYA, KUNA, being the student council president, drama, band, choir, and several sports. My favorite subject in school is Language Arts. This year, I have the privilege of taking a language arts class that is based on the Holocaust. Once I'm out of grade school, I plan to go to college to earn my master's and bachelor's degrees in teaching so that I can become a teacher.

I first met Mr. Gray when I was in kindergarten. He was my principal at Foust Elementary School. Everyone loved Mr. Gray so much. He always put others before himself. Mr. Gray completely changed me. He taught me many life lessons and led me toward the right path. I'm grateful to have him as a part of me. In the fourth grade, he sadly, though full of faith, left to live in Africa doing missionary work. Although I missed him very much, I knew he was where God had sent him. After 4 long-awaited years, he came back to Kentucky. He didn't stay for long though. He knew there were families in Mozambique that also needed their lives touched by him.

By knowing Mr. Gray, I have become a better person towards others and myself, and my faith in God has been strengthened. If you ever get the chance to meet him, you'll see why I am so honored to have known him. He's a great man who lives only to reach out and touch as many people as he can. When I look at Mr. Gray, I see someone who truly knows God. I know that when he finally leaves this earth, he will rewarded greatly in heaven and be with his Father forever.

She sits in class day after day. She bothers no one…

Don't Forget Frances.

She walks home alone every day after school…

Don't Forget Frances.

She eats lunch with other kids but she doesn't talk to them and they don't talk to her…

Don't Forget Frances.

She's not at school today and the only person to notice is the attendance clerk.

Don't Forget Frances.

She's not in the crowd on Friday night. Why would she go to the game and sit alone?

She made decent grades but her grades have dropped and no one notices…

Don't Forget Frances.

School Report Card

Frances

Class	Task	Quarters 1st	Quarter
Adv. Language Arts Harrell, B.	Mid Term (4.5 Weeks)	A+	C/82
	Term Grade	A+/99	
	Final Grade		
Algebra I Hooten, D.	Mid Term (4.5 Weeks)	B/86	C/74
	Semester Exam		
	Semester Grade		
	Term Grade		
7800-1 Band Jensen, H.	Mid Term (4.5 Weeks)	A+/99	B/87
	Term Grade		
	Final Grade		
7070-1 Chorus Lawrence, J.	Mid Term (4.5 Weeks)	A+	A+
	Term Grade	A+	
	Final Grade		
3800-2 Science Brown, C.	Mid Term (4.5 Weeks)	A-/93	D/70
	Term Grade		
	Final Grade		
4800-1 Social Studies Shaw, J.	Mid Term (4.5 Weeks)	A+	C/76
	Term Grade		
	Final Grade		
8000-3 Spanish I Brownfield, B.	Mid Term (4.5 Weeks)	A/94	B/85
	Semester Exam		
	Semester Grade		

She's always picked last in gym class...Why do we allow kids to be picked last?

Don't Forget Frances.

She's changing in every way but no one has
noticed and she's freaked out about
it. She's too shy to ask…

Don't Forget Frances.

She's a gifted artist but it's unknown because she only draws at home at night…

Don't Forget Frances.

She isn't called on and she doesn't volunteer...

Don't Forget Frances.

She longs to be part of something bigger than herself…

Don't Forget Frances.

She's slipping through the cracks and no one knows…

Don't Forget Frances.

She struggles with the pressure of the neighborhood and she's leaning toward joining the crowd…

Don't Forget Frances.

She's beautiful, intelligent, and searching for her place in the world. She's also, lonely, confused and forgotten...

Please, Don't Forget Frances!

DON'T FORGET FRANCES!!

DON'T FORGET FRANCES!!